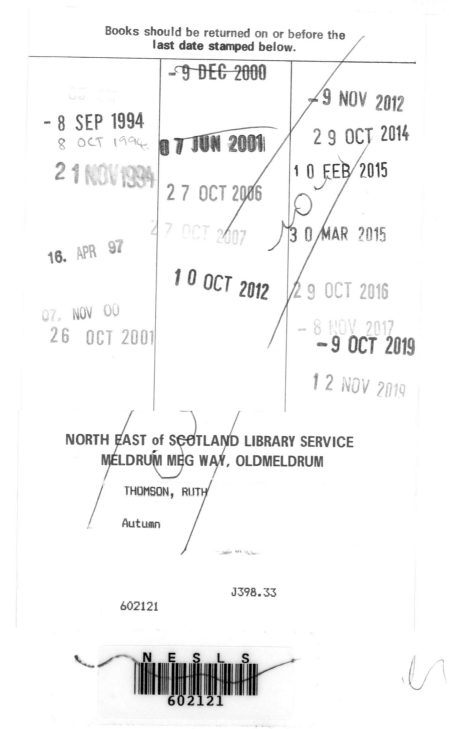

Get set... GO!

Autumn

Ruth Thomson

Contents

It's autumn! 2

A leaf collection 4

Autumn tree collage 6

A leafy face 8

Salt dough models 10

A fruit and seed
collection 12

See how seeds scatter 14

Seed picture 16

Autumn picture 18

Vegetable kebabs 20

Woodland masks 22

Index 24

Watts Books

London • New York • Sydney

It's autumn!

Autumn is a time of change.
The days become shorter and colder
The leaves of trees and bushes turn
orange, yellow and brown and fall off.

The hedgerows are bright
with rosehips and berries.
The ground is littered with acorns
and conkers and other seeds.

Many birds fly away
to warmer countries for the winter.
Squirrels, mice and voles gather
stores of food and bury them.

Bats, frogs, snakes and dormice
find a sheltered place.
They go into a deep sleep,
called hibernation.

A leaf collection

Get ready

- ✔ Leaves
- ✔ Newspaper
- ✔ Heavy books
- ✔ Glue
- ✔ Scrapbook
- ✔ Felt-tip pen

...Get set

Collect all sorts of fallen leaves.
Look carefully to find out
which trees they have come from.

 Go!

Lay the leaves between
two sheets of newspaper.
Put heavy books on top.
After two weeks, the leaves
will be flat and dry.
Glue them in a scrapbook and label them.

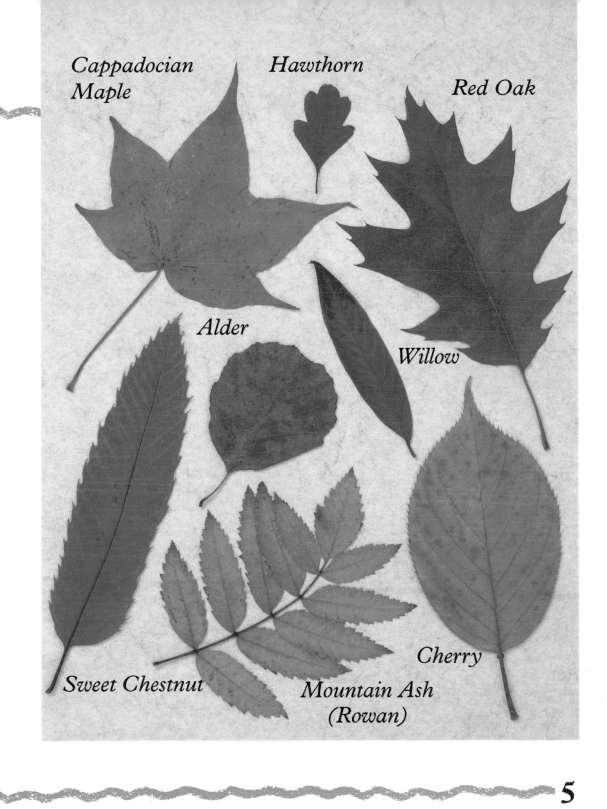

Cappadocian Maple

Hawthorn

Red Oak

Alder

Willow

Sweet Chestnut

Mountain Ash (Rowan)

Cherry

Autumn tree collage

Get ready

- ✔ Strong, thin paper
- ✔ Masking tape
- ✔ Wax crayons
- ✔ Leaves
- ✔ Scissors
- ✔ Glue
- ✔ Blue paper

...Get set

Tape thin paper to a tree trunk.
Rub a wax crayon over it.
A pattern will appear.
Dry some leaves (see page 4).

⟿⟿⟿ *Go!*

Cut out a trunk from your bark rubbing.
Glue it on to the blue paper.
Glue on the dried leaves.

A leafy face

Get ready

- ✔ Sheet of stiff, coloured paper
- ✔ Leaves
- ✔ Glue

...Get set

Dry some leaves (see page 4).
Sort them by colour, size and shape.

Go!

Arrange the leaves on the paper
in the shape of a face.
When you are happy with it,
glue the leaves in position.

Salt dough models

Get ready

- ✔ 2 cups plain flour
- ✔ 1 cup salt
- ✔ 1 cup cold water
- ✔ 2 tablespoons cooking oil
- ✔ Food colourings
- ✔ Baking tray

...Get set

Stir the ingredients in a bowl.
Knead the mixture with your hands.
Make several small balls of dough.
Add drops of food colouring.
Knead until the colour is mixed in.

Go!

Shape the dough and cut and prick it
with a knife or fork to make patterns.
Bake it in the oven on a baking tray
at 300°F/150°C for at least an hour.

A fruit and seed collectio

Get ready

✔ All sorts of fruits and seeds
   from trees, bushes and flowers

...Get set

Open some of the fruit to see
the seeds inside.
Keep pine cones in a warm, dry place.
Soon they will open, so you can see
their seeds.

⊸⊛⊸⊛⊸⊛ *Go!*

Find out the names of
your fruits and seeds.
Label your collection.

Sweet
Chestnuts

Beech fruits

Horse Chestnuts

Plane seeds

Sycamore
wings

Ash
keys

Scots Pine
cones

Broom pods

Birch
seeds

Oak
acorns

Ivy seeds

Rosehips

13

See how seeds scatter

Get ready

✔ All sorts of fruit and seeds

...Get set

Sort your collection into groups.

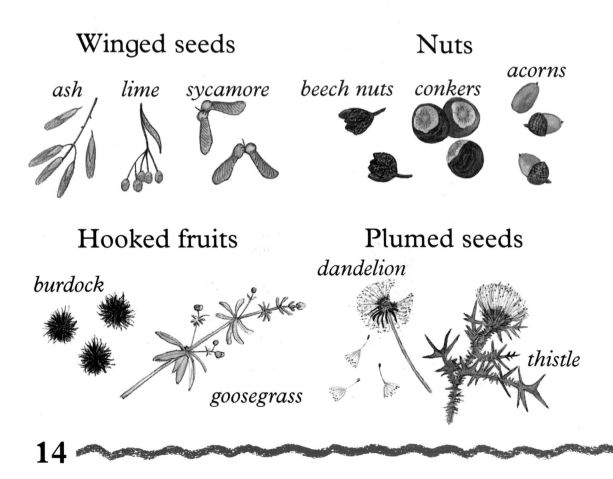

Winged seeds

ash *lime* *sycamore*

Nuts

beech nuts *conkers* *acorns*

Hooked fruits

burdock

goosegrass

Plumed seeds

dandelion

thistle

=ᗡ=ᗡ=ᗡ ***Go!***

Throw winged seeds up in the air. Measure how far they travel.

See how nuts are protected. Count the seeds in each case.

See what hooked fruits cling to. Try wood, fur, wool, plastic and metal.

Blow a plumed seed head. Watch where the seeds go.

Seed picture

Get ready

- ✔ Flat seeds: ash, sycamore, elm, pumpkin, sunflower
- ✔ Sheet of stiff paper
- ✔ Pencil
- ✔ Glue

...Get set

Draw the outline of a picture
faintly, in pencil.
Spread glue inside it.
Sort your seeds by size and shape.

⇒🌫 ⇒🌫 ⇒🌫 *Go!*

Stick seeds on to your picture.
Start at the edges and cover the outline.

Autumn picture

Get ready

- ✔ 1 m of 1"(2.5 cm) wide wood
- ✔ Nails
- ✔ Hammer
- ✔ Wood glue
- ✔ Wood stain or paint
- ✔ Stapler
- ✔ Leaves, twigs, seeds, berries
- ✔ String

...Get set

Ask an adult to cut the wood into four equal pieces.
Nail and glue it to make a frame.
Paint or stain it.

 Go!

Staple leaves, twigs and seeds on to the back of the frame.
Hang berries on some string.

Vegetable kebabs

Get ready

- ✔ Peppers
- ✔ Courgettes
- ✔ Mushrooms
- ✔ Cherry tomatoes

- ✔ Baby sweetcorn
- ✔ Olive oil
- ✔ Lemon
- ✔ Lemon squeezer

- ✔ Knife
- ✔ Tablespoon
- ✔ Dish
- ✔ Skewers

...Get set

Chop the courgettes and peppers.
Pour 3 spoons of oil into the dish.
Cut the lemon in half and squeeze it.
Mix 3 spoons of the juice with the oil.
Soak the vegetables in this mixture for 2 hours.

Go!

Thread the vegetables on to skewers.
Grill them for 8 minutes, turning often.

Woodland masks

Get ready

✔ Newspaper torn into strips

✔ Large balloon

✔ Wallpaper paste

✔ Scissors

✔ Paints and paintbrush

✔ Thin elastic

✔ Leaves, seeds and feathers to decorate

...Get set

Paste several layers of newspaper strips over half a blown-up balloon. Leave them to dry for several days.

Go!

Take out the balloon.
Cut eye, nose and mouth holes in the mask.
Paint and decorate it.
Make a hole on either side.
Thread the elastic through and knot it.

Index

acorn 2, 13, 14
ash 13, 14, 16

berries 2, 18
bird 2

conker 2, 14

dandelion 14

fruits 12

hibernation 2
  hibernating
    animals 2

leaf 2, 4, 6, 8,
  18, 22

dried leaves 4,
  6, 8
leaf collection 4
leafy face 8

mask 22
  woodland
    masks 22
mice 2

pine cones 12, 13

rosehip 2, 13

seeds 2, 12, 14
  16, 18, 22
how seeds
  scatter 14

seed collection
  12
seed picture 16
sycamore 13,
  14, 16
sunflower 14
squirrel 2

thistle 14
tree 2, 6
  tree collage 6

vegetable kebabs
  20
vole 2

Photographic credits:
Heather Angel 15tl, tr, br;
Chris Fairclough Colour
Library 3, 21; Peter Millard 5, 7,
9, 11, 13, 17, 19.

©1993 Watts Books

Watts Books

96 Leonard Street
London EC2A 4RH

Franklin Watts Australia
14 Mars Road
Lane Cove
NSW 2066

UK ISBN 0 7496 1302 5

10 9 8 7 6 5 4 3 2 1

Editor: Pippa Pollard
Design: Ruth Levy
Cover design: Mike Davis
Artwork: Ruth Levy

A CIP catalogue record for this
book is available from the
British Library

Dewey Decimal Classification
745.5

Printed in Malaysia